LANDSCAPES

2021

Published by Danilo Promotions Ltd., EN9 1AS, England. Printed in South Korea.

Contact Danilo for a full listing of our complete range of Calendars, Diaries and Greeting Cards or find us on the internet:
www.danilo.com or email us at: **sales@danilo.com**

/DaniloCalendarsUK **@CalendarsUK**

PERSONAL INFORMATION

Name

Address

Mobile

Email

IN CASE OF EMERGENCY PLEASE CONTACT

Name

Address

Mobile

Doctor

Doctor Telephone

Known Allergies

2020

JANUARY

WK	M	T	W	T	F	S	S
1			1	2	3	4	5
2	6	7	8	9	10	11	12
3	13	14	15	16	17	18	19
4	20	21	22	23	24	25	26
5	27	28	29	30	31		

FEBRUARY

WK	M	T	W	T	F	S	S
5						1	2
6	3	4	5	6	7	8	9
7	10	11	12	13	14	15	16
8	17	18	19	20	21	22	23
9	24	25	26	27	28	29	

MARCH

WK	M	T	W	T	F	S	S
9							1
10	2	3	4	5	6	7	8
11	9	10	11	12	13	14	15
12	16	17	18	19	20	21	22
13	23	24	25	26	27	28	29
14	30	31					

APRIL

WK	M	T	W	T	F	S	S
14			1	2	3	4	5
15	6	7	8	9	10	11	12
16	13	14	15	16	17	18	19
17	20	21	22	23	24	25	26
18	27	28	29	30			

MAY

WK	M	T	W	T	F	S	S
18					1	2	3
19	4	5	6	7	8	9	10
20	11	12	13	14	15	16	17
21	18	19	20	21	22	23	24
22	25	26	27	28	29	30	31

JUNE

WK	M	T	W	T	F	S	S
23	1	2	3	4	5	6	7
24	8	9	10	11	12	13	14
25	15	16	17	18	19	20	21
26	22	23	24	25	26	27	28
27	29	30					

JULY

WK	M	T	W	T	F	S	S
27			1	2	3	4	5
28	6	7	8	9	10	11	12
29	13	14	15	16	17	18	19
30	20	21	22	23	24	25	26
31	27	28	29	30	31		

AUGUST

WK	M	T	W	T	F	S	S
31						1	2
32	3	4	5	6	7	8	9
33	10	11	12	13	14	15	16
34	17	18	19	20	21	22	23
35	24	25	26	27	28	29	30
36	31						

SEPTEMBER

WK	M	T	W	T	F	S	S
36		1	2	3	4	5	6
37	7	8	9	10	11	12	13
38	14	15	16	17	18	19	20
39	21	22	23	24	25	26	27
40	28	29	30				

OCTOBER

WK	M	T	W	T	F	S	S
40				1	2	3	4
41	5	6	7	8	9	10	11
42	12	13	14	15	16	17	18
43	19	20	21	22	23	24	25
44	26	27	28	29	30	31	

NOVEMBER

WK	M	T	W	T	F	S	S
44							1
45	2	3	4	5	6	7	8
46	9	10	11	12	13	14	15
47	16	17	18	19	20	21	22
48	23	24	25	26	27	28	29
49	30						

DECEMBER

WK	M	T	W	T	F	S	S
49		1	2	3	4	5	6
50	7	8	9	10	11	12	13
51	14	15	16	17	18	19	20
52	21	22	23	24	25	26	27
53	28	29	30	31			

JANUARY

WK	M	T	W	T	F	S	S
53					1	2	3
1	4	5	6	7	8	9	10
2	11	12	13	14	15	16	17
3	18	19	20	21	22	23	24
4	25	26	27	28	29	30	31

FEBRUARY

WK	M	T	W	T	F	S	S
5	1	2	3	4	5	6	7
6	8	9	10	11	12	13	14
7	15	16	17	18	19	20	21
8	22	23	24	25	26	27	28

MARCH

WK	M	T	W	T	F	S	S
9	1	2	3	4	5	6	7
10	8	9	10	11	12	13	14
11	15	16	17	18	19	20	21
12	22	23	24	25	26	27	28
13	29	30	31				

APRIL

WK	M	T	W	T	F	S	S
13				1	2	3	4
14	5	6	7	8	9	10	11
15	12	13	14	15	16	17	18
16	19	20	21	22	23	24	25
17	26	27	28	29	30		

MAY

WK	M	T	W	T	F	S	S
17						1	2
18	3	4	5	6	7	8	9
19	10	11	12	13	14	15	16
20	17	18	19	20	21	22	23
21	24	25	26	27	28	29	30
22	31						

JUNE

WK	M	T	W	T	F	S	S
22		1	2	3	4	5	6
23	7	8	9	10	11	12	13
24	14	15	16	17	18	19	20
25	21	22	23	24	25	26	27
26	28	29	30				

JULY

WK	M	T	W	T	F	S	S
26				1	2	3	4
27	5	6	7	8	9	10	11
28	12	13	14	15	16	17	18
29	19	20	21	22	23	24	25
30	26	27	28	29	30	31	

AUGUST

WK	M	T	W	T	F	S	S
30							1
31	2	3	4	5	6	7	8
32	9	10	11	12	13	14	15
33	16	17	18	19	20	21	22
34	23	24	25	26	27	28	29
35	30	31					

SEPTEMBER

WK	M	T	W	T	F	S	S
35			1	2	3	4	5
36	6	7	8	9	10	11	12
37	13	14	15	16	17	18	19
38	20	21	22	23	24	25	26
39	27	28	29	30			

OCTOBER

WK	M	T	W	T	F	S	S
39					1	2	3
40	4	5	6	7	8	9	10
41	11	12	13	14	15	16	17
42	18	19	20	21	22	23	24
43	25	26	27	28	29	30	31

NOVEMBER

WK	M	T	W	T	F	S	S
44	1	2	3	4	5	6	7
45	8	9	10	11	12	13	14
46	15	16	17	18	19	20	21
47	22	23	24	25	26	27	28
48	29	30					

DECEMBER

WK	M	T	W	T	F	S	S
48			1	2	3	4	5
49	6	7	8	9	10	11	12
50	13	14	15	16	17	18	19
51	20	21	22	23	24	25	26
52	27	28	29	30	31		

2022

JANUARY

WK	M	T	W	T	F	S	S
52						1	2
1	3	4	5	6	7	8	9
2	10	11	12	13	14	15	16
3	17	18	19	20	21	22	23
4	24	25	26	27	28	29	30
5	31						

FEBRUARY

WK	M	T	W	T	F	S	S
5		1	2	3	4	5	6
6	7	8	9	10	11	12	13
7	14	15	16	17	18	19	20
8	21	22	23	24	25	26	27
9	28						

MARCH

WK	M	T	W	T	F	S	S
9		1	2	3	4	5	6
10	7	8	9	10	11	12	13
11	14	15	16	17	18	19	20
12	21	22	23	24	25	26	27
13	28	29	30	31			

APRIL

WK	M	T	W	T	F	S	S
13					1	2	3
14	4	5	6	7	8	9	10
15	11	12	13	14	15	16	17
16	18	19	20	21	22	23	24
17	25	26	27	28	29	30	

MAY

WK	M	T	W	T	F	S	S
17							1
18	2	3	4	5	6	7	8
19	9	10	11	12	13	14	15
20	16	17	18	19	20	21	22
21	23	24	25	26	27	28	29
22	30	31					

JUNE

WK	M	T	W	T	F	S	S
22			1	2	3	4	5
23	6	7	8	9	10	11	12
24	13	14	15	16	17	18	19
25	20	21	22	23	24	25	26
26	27	28	29	30			

JULY

WK	M	T	W	T	F	S	S
26					1	2	3
27	4	5	6	7	8	9	10
28	11	12	13	14	15	16	17
29	18	19	20	21	22	23	24
30	25	26	27	28	29	30	31

AUGUST

WK	M	T	W	T	F	S	S
31	1	2	3	4	5	6	7
32	8	9	10	11	12	13	14
33	15	16	17	18	19	20	21
34	22	23	24	25	26	27	28
35	29	30	31				

SEPTEMBER

WK	M	T	W	T	F	S	S
35				1	2	3	4
36	5	6	7	8	9	10	11
37	12	13	14	15	16	17	18
38	19	20	21	22	23	24	25
39	26	27	28	29	30		

OCTOBER

WK	M	T	W	T	F	S	S
39						1	2
40	3	4	5	6	7	8	9
41	10	11	12	13	14	15	16
42	17	18	19	20	21	22	23
43	24	25	26	27	28	29	30
44	31						

NOVEMBER

WK	M	T	W	T	F	S	S
44		1	2	3	4	5	6
45	7	8	9	10	11	12	13
46	14	15	16	17	18	19	20
47	21	22	23	24	25	26	27
48	28	29	30				

DECEMBER

WK	M	T	W	T	F	S	S
48				1	2	3	4
49	5	6	7	8	9	10	11
50	12	13	14	15	16	17	18
51	19	20	21	22	23	24	25
52	26	27	28	29	30	31	

	2021
New Year's Day	JAN 1
Bank Holiday (Scotland)	JAN 4
Chinese New Year (Ox)	FEB 12
St. Valentine's Day	FEB 14
Shrove Tuesday	FEB 16
St. David's Day (Wales)	MAR 1
World Book Day	MAR 4
Mothering Sunday	MAR 14
St. Patrick's Day	MAR 17
Passover Begins	MAR 28
Daylight Saving Time Starts	MAR 28
Good Friday (UK)	APR 2
Easter Sunday	APR 4
Easter Monday	APR 5
Ramadan Starts	APR 13
St. George's Day	APR 23
Early May Bank Holiday	MAY 3
Spring Bank Holiday	MAY 31
Father's Day	JUN 20
Battle of the Boyne (Northern Ireland)	JUL 12
Summer Bank Holiday (Scotland)	AUG 2
Islamic New Year	AUG 10
Summer Bank Holiday (ENG, NIR, WAL)	AUG 30
Rosh Hashanah (Jewish New Year) Begins	SEP 6
Yom Kippur (Day of Atonement) Begins	SEP 15
The United Nations International Day of Peace	SEP 21
World Mental Health Day	OCT 10
Daylight Saving Time Ends	OCT 31
Halloween	OCT 31
Diwali	NOV 4
Guy Fawkes Night	NOV 5
Remembrance Sunday	NOV 14
St. Andrew's Day (Scotland)	NOV 30
Christmas Day	DEC 25
Boxing Day	DEC 26
Bank Holiday	DEC 27
Bank Holiday	DEC 28
New Year's Eve	DEC 31

JANUARY	FEBRUARY	MARCH
1 F	1 M	1 M
2 S	2 T	2 T
3 S	3 W	3 W
4 M	4 T	4 T
5 T	5 F	5 F
6 W	**6 S**	**6 S**
7 T	**7 S**	**7 S**
8 F	8 M	8 M
9 S	9 T	9 T
10 S	10 W	10 W
11 M	11 T	11 T
12 T	12 F	12 F
13 W	**13 S**	**13 S**
14 T	**14 S**	**14 S**
15 F	15 M	15 M
16 S	16 T	16 T
17 S	17 W	17 W
18 M	18 T	18 T
19 T	19 F	19 F
20 W	**20 S**	**20 S**
21 T	**21 S**	**21 S**
22 F	22 M	22 M
23 S	23 T	23 T
24 S	24 W	24 W
25 M	25 T	25 T
26 T	26 F	26 F
27 W	**27 S**	**27 S**
28 T	**28 S**	**28 S**
29 F		29 M
30 S		30 T
31 S		31 W

APRIL	MAY	JUNE
1 T	**1 S**	1 T
2 F	**2 S**	2 W
3 S	3 M	3 T
4 S	4 T	4 F
5 M	5 W	**5 S**
6 T	6 T	**6 S**
7 W	7 F	7 M
8 T	**8 S**	8 T
9 F	**9 S**	9 W
10 S	10 M	10 T
11 S	11 T	11 F
12 M	12 W	**12 S**
13 T	13 T	**13 S**
14 W	14 F	14 M
15 T	**15 S**	15 T
16 F	**16 S**	16 W
17 S	17 M	17 T
18 S	18 T	18 F
19 M	19 W	**19 S**
20 T	20 T	**20 S**
21 W	21 F	21 M
22 T	**22 S**	22 T
23 F	**23 S**	23 W
24 S	24 M	24 T
25 S	25 T	25 F
26 M	26 W	**26 S**
27 T	27 T	**27 S**
28 W	28 F	28 M
29 T	**29 S**	29 T
30 F	**30 S**	30 W
	31 M	

JULY	AUGUST	SEPTEMBER
1 T	**1 S**	1 W
2 F	2 M	2 T
3 S	3 T	3 F
4 S	4 W	**4 S**
5 M	5 T	**5 S**
6 T	6 F	6 M
7 W	**7 S**	7 T
8 T	**8 S**	8 W
9 F	9 M	9 T
10 S	10 T	10 F
11 S	11 W	**11 S**
12 M	12 T	**12 S**
13 T	13 F	13 M
14 W	**14 S**	14 T
15 T	**15 S**	15 W
16 F	16 M	16 T
17 S	17 T	17 F
18 S	18 W	**18 S**
19 M	19 T	**19 S**
20 T	20 F	20 M
21 W	**21 S**	21 T
22 T	**22 S**	22 W
23 F	23 M	23 T
24 S	24 T	24 F
25 S	25 W	**25 S**
26 M	26 T	**26 S**
27 T	27 F	27 M
28 W	**28 S**	28 T
29 T	**29 S**	29 W
30 F	30 M	30 T
31 S	31 T	

OCTOBER	NOVEMBER	DECEMBER
1 F	1 M	1 W
2 S	2 T	2 T
3 S	3 W	3 F
4 M	4 T	**4 S**
5 T	5 F	**5 S**
6 W	**6 S**	6 M
7 T	**7 S**	7 T
8 F	8 M	8 W
9 S	9 T	9 T
10 S	10 W	10 F
11 M	11 T	**11 S**
12 T	12 F	**12 S**
13 W	**13 S**	13 M
14 T	**14 S**	14 T
15 F	15 M	15 W
16 S	16 T	16 T
17 S	17 W	17 F
18 M	18 T	**18 S**
19 T	19 F	**19 S**
20 W	**20 S**	20 M
21 T	**21 S**	21 T
22 F	22 M	22 W
23 S	23 T	23 T
24 S	24 W	24 F
25 M	25 T	**25 S**
26 T	26 F	**26 S**
27 W	**27 S**	27 M
28 T	**28 S**	28 T
29 F	29 M	29 W
30 S	30 T	30 T
31 S		31 F

BBC earth

JANUARY

Stars and trees in the dry season, Sri Lanka. This photograph was captured in Yala National Park, a huge area of forest, grasslands and wetlands bordering the Indian Ocean, in southeast Sri Lanka. With few major settlements close by the location enjoys some of the darkest skies in the region.

28 MONDAY

Boxing Day Bank Holiday (UK)

29 TUESDAY

30 WEDNESDAY

31 THURSDAY

New Year's Eve

New Year's Day — FRIDAY 1

SATURDAY 2

SUNDAY 3

NOTES

W	T	F	S	S	M	T	W	T	F	S	S	**M**	**T**	**W**	**T**	**F**	**S**	**S**	M	T	W	T	F	S	S	M	T	W	T	F
16	17	18	19	20	21	22	23	24	25	26	27	**28**	**29**	**30**	**31**	**1**	**2**	**3**	4	5	6	7	8	9	10	11	12	13	14	15

4 MONDAY Bank Holiday (Scotland)

5 TUESDAY

6 WEDNESDAY

7 THURSDAY

FRIDAY 8

SATURDAY 9

SUNDAY 10

NOTES

BBC earth

F	S	S	**M**	**T**	**W**	**T**	**F**	**S**	**S**	M	T	W	T	F	S	S	M	T	W	T	F	S	S	M	T	W	T	F	S	S
1	2	3	**4**	**5**	**6**	**7**	**8**	**9**	**10**	11	12	13	14	15	16	17	18	19	20	21	22	23	24	25	26	27	28	29	30	31

11 MONDAY

12 TUESDAY

13 WEDNESDAY

14 THURSDAY

FRIDAY 15

SATURDAY 16

SUNDAY 17

NOTES

BBC earth

F	S	S	M	T	W	T	F	S	S	**M**	**T**	**W**	**T**	**F**	**S**	**S**	M	T	W	T	F	S	S	M	T	W	T	F	S	S
1	2	3	4	5	6	7	8	9	10	**11**	**12**	**13**	**14**	**15**	**16**	**17**	18	19	20	21	22	23	24	25	26	27	28	29	30	31

18 MONDAY

19 TUESDAY

20 WEDNESDAY

21 THURSDAY

FRIDAY 22

SATURDAY 23

SUNDAY 24

NOTES

BBC earth

F	S	S	M	T	W	T	F	S	S	M	T	W	T	F	S	S	**M**	**T**	**W**	**T**	**F**	**S**	**S**	M	T	W	T	F	S	S
1	2	3	4	5	6	7	8	9	10	11	12	13	14	15	16	17	**18**	**19**	**20**	**21**	**22**	**23**	**24**	25	26	27	28	29	30	31

25 MONDAY

26 TUESDAY

27 WEDNESDAY

28 THURSDAY

FRIDAY 29

SATURDAY 30

SUNDAY 31

NOTES

BBC earth

F	S	S	M	T	W	T	F	S	S	M	T	W	T	F	S	S	M	T	W	T	F	S	S	**M**	**T**	**W**	**T**	**F**	**S**	**S**
1	2	3	4	5	6	7	8	9	10	11	12	13	14	15	16	17	18	19	20	21	22	23	24	**25**	**26**	**27**	**28**	**29**	**30**	**31**

Mount Merapi volcano towers behind the ancient Borobudur Buddhist temple, central Java. Of Indonesia's 130 active volcanoes, Mount Merapi is the most active. Its name means 'Mountain of Fire' and it stands at 9,551 feet (2,911 metres) tall.

BBC earth

FEBRUARY

1 MONDAY

2 TUESDAY

3 WEDNESDAY

4 THURSDAY

FRIDAY 5

SATURDAY 6

SUNDAY 7

NOTES

BBC earth

M	T	W	T	F	S	S	M	T	W	T	F	S	S	M	T	W	T	F	S	S	M	T	W	T	F	S	S
1	**2**	**3**	**4**	**5**	**6**	**7**	8	9	10	11	12	13	14	15	16	17	18	19	20	21	22	23	24	25	26	27	28

F

8 MONDAY

9 TUESDAY

10 WEDNESDAY

11 THURSDAY

Chinese New Year (Ox)

FRIDAY 12

SATURDAY 13

St. Valentine's Day

SUNDAY 14

NOTES

BBC earth

M	T	W	T	F	S	S	**M**	**T**	**W**	**T**	**F**	**S**	**S**	M	T	W	T	F	S	S	M	T	W	T	F	S	S
1	2	3	4	5	6	7	**8**	**9**	**10**	**11**	**12**	**13**	**14**	15	16	17	18	19	20	21	22	23	24	25	26	27	28

F

15 MONDAY

16 TUESDAY

Shrove Tuesday

17 WEDNESDAY

18 THURSDAY

F

FRIDAY 19

SATURDAY 20

SUNDAY 21

NOTES

BBC earth

M	T	W	T	F	S	S	M	T	W	T	F	S	S	**M**	**T**	**W**	**T**	**F**	**S**	**S**	M	T	W	T	F	S	S
1	2	3	4	5	6	7	8	9	10	11	12	13	14	**15**	**16**	**17**	**18**	**19**	**20**	**21**	22	23	24	25	26	27	28

22 MONDAY

23 TUESDAY

24 WEDNESDAY

25 THURSDAY

F

FRIDAY 26

SATURDAY 27

SUNDAY 28

NOTES

BBC earth

M	T	W	T	F	S	S	M	T	W	T	F	S	S	M	T	W	T	F	S	S	**M**	**T**	**W**	**T**	**F**	**S**	**S**
1	2	3	4	5	6	7	8	9	10	11	12	13	14	15	16	17	18	19	20	21	**22**	**23**	**24**	**25**	**26**	**27**	**28**

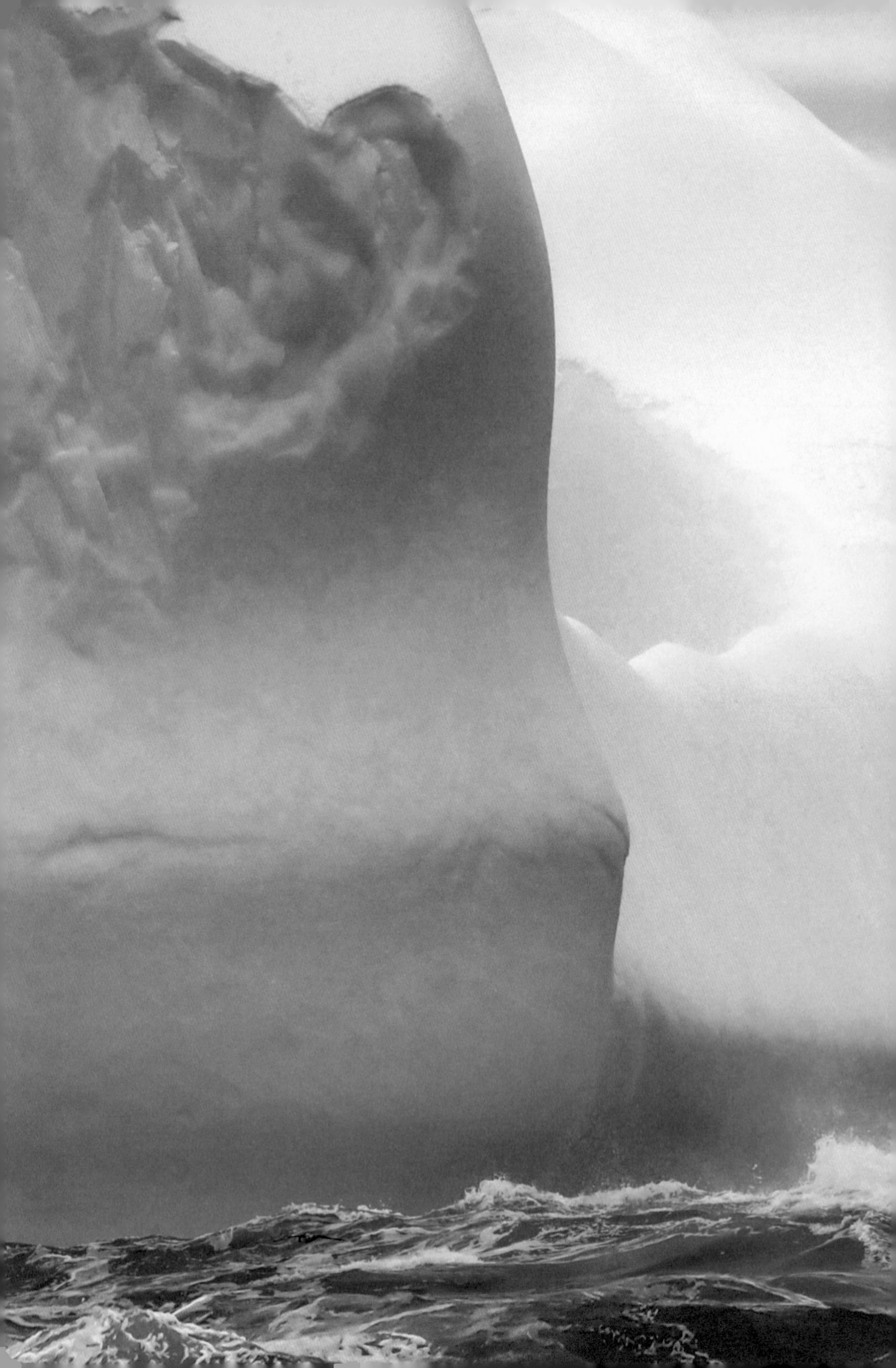

BBC earth

MARCH

North coast of South Georgia. Sub-Antarctic island icebergs with a small flock of storm petrels darting around the waves that lapped up against their sides.

1 MONDAY St. David's Day (Wales)

2 TUESDAY

3 WEDNESDAY

4 THURSDAY World Book Day

FRIDAY 5

SATURDAY 6

SUNDAY 7

NOTES

BBC earth

M	T	W	T	F	S	S	M	T	W	T	F	S	S	M	T	W	T	F	S	S	M	T	W	T	F	S	S	M	T	W
1	**2**	**3**	**4**	**5**	**6**	**7**	8	9	10	11	12	13	14	15	16	17	18	19	20	21	22	23	24	25	26	27	28	29	30	31

8 MONDAY

9 TUESDAY

10 WEDNESDAY

11 THURSDAY

FRIDAY 12

SATURDAY 13

Mothering Sunday

SUNDAY 14

NOTES

BBC earth

M	T	W	T	F	S	S	**M**	**T**	**W**	**T**	**F**	**S**	**S**	M	T	W	T	F	S	S	M	T	W	T	F	S	S	M	T	W
1	2	3	4	5	6	7	**8**	**9**	**10**	**11**	**12**	**13**	**14**	15	16	17	18	19	20	21	22	23	24	25	26	27	28	29	30	31

15 MONDAY

16 TUESDAY

17 WEDNESDAY

St. Patrick's Day

18 THURSDAY

FRIDAY 19

SATURDAY 20

SUNDAY 21

NOTES

BBC earth

M	T	W	T	F	S	S	M	T	W	T	F	S	S	**M**	**T**	**W**	**T**	**F**	**S**	**S**	M	T	W	T	F	S	S	M	T	W
1	2	3	4	5	6	7	8	9	10	11	12	13	14	**15**	**16**	**17**	**18**	**19**	**20**	**21**	22	23	24	25	26	27	28	29	30	31

22 MONDAY

23 TUESDAY

24 WEDNESDAY

25 THURSDAY

FRIDAY 26

SATURDAY 27

SUNDAY 28

Passover Begins / Daylight Saving Time Starts

NOTES

BBC earth

M	T	W	T	F	S	S	M	T	W	T	F	S	S	M	T	W	T	F	S	S	**M**	**T**	**W**	**T**	**F**	**S**	**S**	M	T	W
1	2	3	4	5	6	7	8	9	10	11	12	13	14	15	16	17	18	19	20	21	**22**	**23**	**24**	**25**	**26**	**27**	**28**	29	30	31

BBC earth

APRIL

Shark Bay, Australia. The vast seagrass meadows of Shark Bay, Australia, are some of the largest in the world. The meadows are comprised of many species, including the seagrass *Amphibolis antarctica*, which support great populations of grazers, such as dugongs and green turtles, as well as their predator, the tiger shark.

29 MONDAY

30 TUESDAY

31 WEDNESDAY

1 THURSDAY

Good Friday (UK) FRIDAY 2

SATURDAY 3

Easter Sunday SUNDAY 4

NOTES

BBC earth

T	W	T	F	S	S	M	T	W	T	F	S	S	**M**	**T**	**W**	**T**	**F**	**S**	**S**	M	T	W	T	F	S	S	M	T	W	T
16	17	18	19	20	21	22	23	24	25	26	27	28	**29**	**30**	**31**	**1**	**2**	**3**	**4**	5	6	7	8	9	10	11	12	13	14	15

5 MONDAY Easter Monday

6 TUESDAY

7 WEDNESDAY

8 THURSDAY

FRIDAY **9**

SATURDAY **10**

SUNDAY **11**

NOTES

T	F	S	S	**M**	**T**	**W**	**T**	**F**	**S**	**S**	M	T	W	T	F	S	S	M	T	W	T	F	S	S	M	T	W	T	F
1	2	3	4	**5**	**6**	**7**	**8**	**9**	**10**	**11**	12	13	14	15	16	17	18	19	20	21	22	23	24	25	26	27	28	29	30

A

12 MONDAY

13 TUESDAY

Ramadan Starts

14 WEDNESDAY

15 THURSDAY

FRIDAY 16

SATURDAY 17

SUNDAY 18

NOTES

BBC earth

T	F	S	S	M	T	W	T	F	S	S	**M**	**T**	**W**	**T**	**F**	**S**	**S**	M	T	W	T	F	S	S	M	T	W	T	F
1	2	3	4	5	6	7	8	9	10	11	**12**	**13**	**14**	**15**	**16**	**17**	**18**	19	20	21	22	23	24	25	26	27	28	29	30

19 MONDAY

20 TUESDAY

21 WEDNESDAY

22 THURSDAY

St. George's Day

FRIDAY 23

SATURDAY 24

SUNDAY 25

NOTES

BBC earth

T	F	S	S	M	T	W	T	F	S	S	M	T	W	T	F	S	S	**M**	**T**	**W**	**T**	**F**	**S**	**S**	M	T	W	T	F
1	2	3	4	5	6	7	8	9	10	11	12	13	14	15	16	17	18	**19**	**20**	**21**	**22**	**23**	**24**	**25**	26	27	28	29	30

BBC earth

MAY

The aurora borealis over an abandoned house, Maine, USA. This all-natural light show, otherwise known as the Northern Lights, staged a dazzling display of greens and yellows over the state of New England in the Autumn of 2015. It was one of the brightest solar events to be witnessed here for many years.

26 MONDAY

27 TUESDAY

28 WEDNESDAY

29 THURSDAY

FRIDAY 30

SATURDAY 1

M

SUNDAY 2

NOTES

BBC earth

F	S	S	M	T	W	T	F	S	S	**M**	**T**	**W**	**T**	**F**	**S**	**S**	M	T	W	T	F	S	S	M	T	W	T	F	S
16	17	18	19	20	21	22	23	24	25	**26**	**27**	**28**	**29**	**30**	**1**	**2**	3	4	5	6	7	8	9	10	11	12	13	14	15

3 MONDAY

Early May Bank Holiday

4 TUESDAY

5 WEDNESDAY

6 THURSDAY

FRIDAY 7

SATURDAY 8

SUNDAY 9

NOTES

BBC earth

S	S	**M**	**T**	**W**	**T**	**F**	**S**	**S**	M	T	W	T	F	S	S	M	T	W	T	F	S	S	M	T	W	T	F	S	S	M
1	2	**3**	**4**	**5**	**6**	**7**	**8**	**9**	10	11	12	13	14	15	16	17	18	19	20	21	22	23	24	25	26	27	28	29	30	31

10 MONDAY

11 TUESDAY

12 WEDNESDAY

13 THURSDAY

FRIDAY 14

SATURDAY 15

SUNDAY 16

NOTES

BBC earth

S	S	M	T	W	T	F	S	S	**M**	**T**	**W**	**T**	**F**	**S**	**S**	M	T	W	T	F	S	S	M	T	W	T	F	S	S	M
1	2	3	4	5	6	7	8	9	**10**	**11**	**12**	**13**	**14**	**15**	**16**	17	18	19	20	21	22	23	24	25	26	27	28	29	30	31

17 MONDAY

18 TUESDAY

19 WEDNESDAY

20 THURSDAY

FRIDAY 21

SATURDAY 22

M

SUNDAY 23

NOTES

BBC earth

S	S	M	T	W	T	F	S	S	M	T	W	T	F	S	S	**M**	**T**	**W**	**T**	**F**	**S**	**S**	M	T	W	T	F	S	S	M
1	2	3	4	5	6	7	8	9	10	11	12	13	14	15	16	**17**	**18**	**19**	**20**	**21**	**22**	**23**	24	25	26	27	28	29	30	31

24 MONDAY

25 TUESDAY

26 WEDNESDAY

27 THURSDAY

FRIDAY 28

SATURDAY 29

M

SUNDAY 30

NOTES

BBC earth

S	S	M	T	W	T	F	S	S	M	T	W	T	F	S	S	M	T	W	T	F	S	S	**M**	**T**	**W**	**T**	**F**	**S**	**S**	M
1	2	3	4	5	6	7	8	9	10	11	12	13	14	15	16	17	18	19	20	21	22	23	**24**	**25**	**26**	**27**	**28**	**29**	**30**	31

BBC earth

JUNE

Paradise Bay, Antarctic Peninsula. Huge sculptural icebergs cast their reflections in the calm, almost black waters of the beautiful Paradise Bay, a harbour located on the western coast of the Antarctic Peninsula. The continent's glaciated mountains loom in the distance.

31 MONDAY

Spring Bank Holiday

1 TUESDAY

2 WEDNESDAY

3 THURSDAY

FRIDAY 4

SATURDAY 5

SUNDAY 6

NOTES

BBC earth

S	M	T	W	T	F	S	S	M	T	W	T	F	S	S	**M**	**T**	**W**	**T**	**F**	**S**	**S**	M	T	W	T	F	S	S	M	T
16	17	18	19	20	21	22	23	24	25	26	27	28	29	30	**31**	**1**	**2**	**3**	**4**	**5**	**6**	7	8	9	10	11	12	13	14	15

J

7 MONDAY

8 TUESDAY

9 WEDNESDAY

10 THURSDAY

FRIDAY 11

SATURDAY 12

SUNDAY 13

NOTES

BBC earth

T	W	T	F	S	S	**M**	**T**	**W**	**T**	**F**	**S**	**S**	M	T	W	T	F	S	S	M	T	W	T	F	S	S	M	T	W
1	2	3	4	5	6	**7**	**8**	**9**	**10**	**11**	**12**	**13**	14	15	16	17	18	19	20	21	22	23	24	25	26	27	28	29	30

14 MONDAY

15 TUESDAY

16 WEDNESDAY

17 THURSDAY

FRIDAY **18**

SATURDAY **19**

Father's Day

SUNDAY **20**

NOTES

BBC earth

T	W	T	F	S	S	M	T	W	T	F	S	S	**M**	**T**	**W**	**T**	**F**	**S**	**S**	M	T	W	T	F	S	S	M	T	W
1	2	3	4	5	6	7	8	9	10	11	12	13	**14**	**15**	**16**	**17**	**18**	**19**	**20**	21	22	23	24	25	26	27	28	29	30

21 MONDAY

22 TUESDAY

23 WEDNESDAY

24 THURSDAY

FRIDAY **25**

SATURDAY **26**

SUNDAY **27**

NOTES

BBC earth

T	W	T	F	S	S	M	T	W	T	F	S	S	M	T	W	T	F	S	S	M	T	W	T	F	S	S	M	T	W
1	2	3	4	5	6	7	8	9	10	11	12	13	14	15	16	17	18	19	20	**21**	**22**	**23**	**24**	**25**	**26**	**27**	28	29	30

Northern Lights over Chocorua Lake and Mount Chocorua, New Hampshire, USA. 2016 saw an unusually high level of solar activity resulting in spectacular displays of the aurora borealis across the northern hemisphere. Known as the Northern Lights, this celestial display is formed when charged particles from the sun clash with atoms in the upper atmosphere to release energy in the form of dancing waves of green, purple and red light. At Chocorua Lake, New Hampshire, the still water brightly reflected the most intense Northern Lights that this part of the United States had experienced in more than a decade.

BBC earth

JULY

28 MONDAY

29 TUESDAY

30 WEDNESDAY

1 THURSDAY

FRIDAY **2**

SATURDAY **3**

SUNDAY **4**

NOTES

BBC earth

W	T	F	S	S	M	T	W	T	F	S	S	**M**	**T**	**W**	**T**	**F**	**S**	**S**	M	T	W	T	F	S	S	M	T	W	T
16	17	18	19	20	21	22	23	24	25	26	27	**28**	**29**	**30**	**1**	**2**	**3**	**4**	5	6	7	8	9	10	11	12	13	14	15

5 MONDAY

6 TUESDAY

7 WEDNESDAY

8 THURSDAY

FRIDAY 9

SATURDAY 10

SUNDAY 11

NOTES

BBC earth

T	F	S	S	**M**	**T**	**W**	**T**	**F**	**S**	**S**	M	T	W	T	F	S	S	M	T	W	T	F	S	S	M	T	W	T	F	S
1	2	3	4	**5**	**6**	**7**	**8**	**9**	**10**	**11**	12	13	14	15	16	17	18	19	20	21	22	23	24	25	26	27	28	29	30	31

12 MONDAY

Battle of the Boyne (Northern Ireland)

13 TUESDAY

14 WEDNESDAY

15 THURSDAY

FRIDAY 16

SATURDAY 17

SUNDAY 18

NOTES

BBC earth

T	F	S	S	M	T	W	T	F	S	S	**M**	**T**	**W**	**T**	**F**	**S**	**S**	M	T	W	T	F	S	S	M	T	W	T	F	S
1	2	3	4	5	6	7	8	9	10	11	**12**	**13**	**14**	**15**	**16**	**17**	**18**	19	20	21	22	23	24	25	26	27	28	29	30	31

19 MONDAY

20 TUESDAY

21 WEDNESDAY

22 THURSDAY

FRIDAY 23

SATURDAY 24

SUNDAY 25

NOTES

BBC earth

T	F	S	S	M	T	W	T	F	S	S	M	T	W	T	F	S	S	**M**	**T**	**W**	**T**	**F**	**S**	**S**	M	T	W	T	F	S
1	2	3	4	5	6	7	8	9	10	11	12	13	14	15	16	17	18	**19**	**20**	**21**	**22**	**23**	**24**	**25**	26	27	28	29	30	31

BBC earth

AUGUST

Sand dunes, Namibia. The sand dunes of Namibia in southwest Africa's Namib Desert are strikingly beautiful – and are some of the oldest in the world. They are also some of the largest, and some can reach a staggering 1,000 feet tall (305 metres).

26 MONDAY

27 TUESDAY

28 WEDNESDAY

29 THURSDAY

FRIDAY **30**

SATURDAY **31**

SUNDAY **1**

A

NOTES

BBC earth

F	S	S	M	T	W	T	F	S	S	**M**	**T**	**W**	**T**	**F**	**S**	**S**	M	T	W	T	F	S	S	M	T	W	T	F	S	S
16	17	18	19	20	21	22	23	24	25	**26**	**27**	**28**	**29**	**30**	**31**	**1**	2	3	4	5	6	7	8	9	10	11	12	13	14	15

2 MONDAY

Summer Bank Holiday (Scotland)

3 TUESDAY

4 WEDNESDAY

5 THURSDAY

FRIDAY 6

SATURDAY 7

SUNDAY 8

A

NOTES

BBC earth

S	M	T	W	T	F	S	S	M	T	W	T	F	S	S	M	T	W	T	F	S	S	M	T	W	T	F	S	S	M	T
1	**2**	**3**	**4**	**5**	**6**	**7**	**8**	9	10	11	12	13	14	15	16	17	18	19	20	21	22	23	24	25	26	27	28	29	30	31

9 MONDAY

10 TUESDAY

Islamic New Year

11 WEDNESDAY

12 THURSDAY

FRIDAY 13

SATURDAY 14

SUNDAY 15

NOTES

BBC earth

S	M	T	W	T	F	S	S	**M**	**T**	**W**	**T**	**F**	**S**	**S**	M	T	W	T	F	S	S	M	T	W	T	F	S	S	M	T
1	2	3	4	5	6	7	8	**9**	**10**	**11**	**12**	**13**	**14**	**15**	16	17	18	19	20	21	22	23	24	25	26	27	28	29	30	31

16 MONDAY

17 TUESDAY

18 WEDNESDAY

19 THURSDAY

FRIDAY 20

SATURDAY 21

SUNDAY 22

A

NOTES

BBC earth

S	M	T	W	T	F	S	S	M	T	W	T	F	S	S	**M**	**T**	**W**	**T**	**F**	**S**	**S**	M	T	W	T	F	S	S	M	T
1	2	3	4	5	6	7	8	9	10	11	12	13	14	15	**16**	**17**	**18**	**19**	**20**	**21**	**22**	23	24	25	26	27	28	29	30	31

23 MONDAY

24 TUESDAY

25 WEDNESDAY

26 THURSDAY

FRIDAY 27

SATURDAY 28

SUNDAY 29

A

NOTES

BBC earth

S	M	T	W	T	F	S	S	M	T	W	T	F	S	S	M	T	W	T	F	S	S	**M**	**T**	**W**	**T**	**F**	**S**	**S**	M	T
1	2	3	4	5	6	7	8	9	10	11	12	13	14	15	16	17	18	19	20	21	22	**23**	**24**	**25**	**26**	**27**	**28**	**29**	30	31

A storm approaches during the onset of the wet season, Northern Australia. Some of the world's biggest and most powerful thunderstorms occur in Northern Australia. Giant cumulonimbus clouds that form here can be taller than the world's highest mountains and release over one thousand lightning strikes an hour. With every discharge the air around explodes, at over twenty-five thousand degrees, four times hotter than the surface of the sun.

SEPTEMBER

30 MONDAY

Summer Bank Holiday (ENG, NIR, WAL)

31 TUESDAY

1 WEDNESDAY

2 THURSDAY

FRIDAY 3

SATURDAY 4

SUNDAY 5

NOTES

M	T	W	T	F	S	S	M	T	W	T	F	S	S	**M**	**T**	**W**	**T**	**F**	**S**	**S**	M	T	W	T	F	S	S	M	T	W
16	17	18	19	20	21	22	23	24	25	26	27	28	29	**30**	**31**	**1**	**2**	**3**	**4**	**5**	6	7	8	9	10	11	12	13	14	15

6 MONDAY

Rosh Hashanah (Jewish New Year) Begins

7 TUESDAY

8 WEDNESDAY

9 THURSDAY

FRIDAY **10**

SATURDAY **11**

SUNDAY **12**

NOTES

BBC earth

W	T	F	S	S	**M**	**T**	**W**	**T**	**F**	**S**	**S**	M	T	W	T	F	S	S	M	T	W	T	F	S	S	M	T	W	T
1	2	3	4	5	**6**	**7**	**8**	**9**	**10**	**11**	**12**	13	14	15	16	17	18	19	20	21	22	23	24	25	26	27	28	29	30

13 MONDAY

14 TUESDAY

15 WEDNESDAY

Yom Kippur (Day of Atonement) Begins

16 THURSDAY

FRIDAY 17

SATURDAY 18

SUNDAY 19

S

NOTES

BBC earth

W	T	F	S	S	M	T	W	T	F	S	S	**M**	**T**	**W**	**T**	**F**	**S**	**S**	M	T	W	T	F	S	S	M	T	W	T
1	2	3	4	5	6	7	8	9	10	11	12	**13**	**14**	**15**	**16**	**17**	**18**	**19**	20	21	22	23	24	25	26	27	28	29	30

20 MONDAY

21 TUESDAY

The United Nations International Day of Peace

22 WEDNESDAY

23 THURSDAY

FRIDAY **24**

SATURDAY **25**

SUNDAY **26**

NOTES

BBC earth

W	T	F	S	S	M	T	W	T	F	S	S	M	T	W	T	F	S	S	**M**	**T**	**W**	**T**	**F**	**S**	**S**	M	T	W	T
1	2	3	4	5	6	7	8	9	10	11	12	13	14	15	16	17	18	19	**20**	**21**	**22**	**23**	**24**	**25**	**26**	27	28	29	30

S

A cameraman films a super-flock of 80,000 budgerigars at a waterhole in Central Australia, for the BBC series 'Wonders of the Monsoon'. During the dry season an oasis such as this attracts not only vast numbers of budgies, but their predators, too. Raptors such as brown falcons, black falcons and Australian hobbies all take their chance to catch a meal amongst the swirling kaleidoscope of yellow and green.

BBC earth

OCTOBER

27 MONDAY

28 TUESDAY

29 WEDNESDAY

30 THURSDAY

FRIDAY 1

SATURDAY 2

SUNDAY 3

O

NOTES

BBC earth

T	F	S	S	M	T	W	T	F	S	S	**M**	**T**	**W**	**T**	**F**	**S**	**S**	M	T	W	T	F	S	S	M	T	W	T	F
16	17	18	19	20	21	22	23	24	25	26	**27**	**28**	**29**	**30**	**1**	**2**	**3**	4	5	6	7	8	9	10	11	12	13	14	15

4 MONDAY

5 TUESDAY

6 WEDNESDAY

7 THURSDAY

FRIDAY 8

SATURDAY 9

World Mental Health Day

SUNDAY 10

NOTES

BBC earth

F	S	S	**M**	**T**	**W**	**T**	**F**	**S**	**S**	M	T	W	T	F	S	S	M	T	W	T	F	S	S	M	T	W	T	F	S	S
1	2	3	**4**	**5**	**6**	**7**	**8**	**9**	**10**	11	12	13	14	15	16	17	18	19	20	21	22	23	24	25	26	27	28	29	30	31

11 MONDAY

12 TUESDAY

13 WEDNESDAY

14 THURSDAY

FRIDAY 15

SATURDAY 16

SUNDAY 17

NOTES

BBC earth

F	S	S	M	T	W	T	F	S	S	**M**	**T**	**W**	**T**	**F**	**S**	**S**	M	T	W	T	F	S	S	M	T	W	T	F	S	S
1	2	3	4	5	6	7	8	9	10	**11**	**12**	**13**	**14**	**15**	**16**	**17**	18	19	20	21	22	23	24	25	26	27	28	29	30	31

18 MONDAY

19 TUESDAY

20 WEDNESDAY

21 THURSDAY

FRIDAY 22

SATURDAY 23

SUNDAY 24

NOTES

BBC earth

F	S	S	M	T	W	T	F	S	S	M	T	W	T	F	S	S	**M**	**T**	**W**	**T**	**F**	**S**	**S**	M	T	W	T	F	S	S
1	2	3	4	5	6	7	8	9	10	11	12	13	14	15	16	17	**18**	**19**	**20**	**21**	**22**	**23**	**24**	25	26	27	28	29	30	31

25 MONDAY

26 TUESDAY

27 WEDNESDAY

28 THURSDAY

FRIDAY 29

SATURDAY 30

SUNDAY 31

Daylight Saving Time Ends / Halloween

NOTES

BBC earth

F	S	S	M	T	W	T	F	S	S	M	T	W	T	F	S	S	M	T	W	T	F	S	S	**M**	**T**	**W**	**T**	**F**	**S**	**S**
1	2	3	4	5	6	7	8	9	10	11	12	13	14	15	16	17	18	19	20	21	22	23	24	**25**	**26**	**27**	**28**	**29**	**30**	**31**

BBC earth

NOVEMBER

Jungle tree tops, West Papua, Indonesia. Jungles cover less than six percent of land, but are home to over half the plants and animals on Earth. Only two percent of the sun's rays reach the jungle's forest.

1 MONDAY

2 TUESDAY

3 WEDNESDAY

4 THURSDAY Diwali

Guy Fawkes Night

FRIDAY 5

SATURDAY 6

SUNDAY 7

NOTES

M	T	W	T	F	S	S	M	T	W	T	F	S	S	M	T	W	T	F	S	S	M	T	W	T	F	S	S	M	T
1	**2**	**3**	**4**	**5**	**6**	**7**	8	9	10	11	12	13	14	15	16	17	18	19	20	21	22	23	24	25	26	27	28	29	30

8 MONDAY

9 TUESDAY

10 WEDNESDAY

11 THURSDAY

FRIDAY 12

SATURDAY 13

Remembrance Sunday

SUNDAY 14

NOTES

BBC earth

M	T	W	T	F	S	S	**M**	**T**	**W**	**T**	**F**	**S**	**S**	M	T	W	T	F	S	S	M	T	W	T	F	S	S	M	T
1	2	3	4	5	6	7	**8**	**9**	**10**	**11**	**12**	**13**	**14**	15	16	17	18	19	20	21	22	23	24	25	26	27	28	29	30

15 MONDAY

16 TUESDAY

17 WEDNESDAY

18 THURSDAY

FRIDAY 19

SATURDAY 20

SUNDAY 21

N

NOTES

BBC earth

M	T	W	T	F	S	S	M	T	W	T	F	S	S	**M**	**T**	**W**	**T**	**F**	**S**	**S**	M	T	W	T	F	S	S	M	T
1	2	3	4	5	6	7	8	9	10	11	12	13	14	**15**	**16**	**17**	**18**	**19**	**20**	**21**	22	23	24	25	26	27	28	29	30

22 MONDAY

23 TUESDAY

24 WEDNESDAY

25 THURSDAY

FRIDAY 26

SATURDAY 27

SUNDAY 28

NOTES

BBC earth

M	T	W	T	F	S	S	M	T	W	T	F	S	S	M	T	W	T	F	S	S	**M**	**T**	**W**	**T**	**F**	**S**	**S**	M	T
1	2	3	4	5	6	7	8	9	10	11	12	13	14	15	16	17	18	19	20	21	**22**	**23**	**24**	**25**	**26**	**27**	**28**	29	30

Neko Harbour, an inlet on the Antarctic Peninsula. Famous for its striking glacier, this harbour is located on the Eastern shores of Andvord Bay and offers visitors to Antarctica a chance to step onto the continent itself.

DECEMBER

29 MONDAY

30 TUESDAY

St. Andrew's Day (Scotland)

1 WEDNESDAY

2 THURSDAY

FRIDAY 3

SATURDAY 4

SUNDAY 5

NOTES

BBC earth

T	W	T	F	S	S	M	T	W	T	F	S	S	**M**	**T**	**W**	**T**	**F**	**S**	**S**	M	T	W	T	F	S	S	M	T	W
16	17	18	19	20	21	22	23	24	25	26	27	28	**29**	**30**	**1**	**2**	**3**	**4**	**5**	6	7	8	9	10	11	12	13	14	15

6 MONDAY

7 TUESDAY

8 WEDNESDAY

9 THURSDAY

FRIDAY 10

SATURDAY 11

SUNDAY 12

NOTES

BBC earth

W	T	F	S	S	**M**	**T**	**W**	**T**	**F**	**S**	**S**	M	T	W	T	F	S	S	M	T	W	T	F	S	S	M	T	W	T	F
1	2	3	4	5	**6**	**7**	**8**	**9**	**10**	**11**	**12**	13	14	15	16	17	18	19	20	21	22	23	24	25	26	27	28	29	30	31

13 MONDAY

14 TUESDAY

15 WEDNESDAY

16 THURSDAY

FRIDAY 17

SATURDAY 18

SUNDAY 19

NOTES

BBC earth

W	T	F	S	S	M	T	W	T	F	S	S	**M**	**T**	**W**	**T**	**F**	**S**	**S**	M	T	W	T	F	S	S	M	T	W	T	F
1	2	3	4	5	6	7	8	9	10	11	12	**13**	**14**	**15**	**16**	**17**	**18**	**19**	20	21	22	23	24	25	26	27	28	29	30	31

20 MONDAY

21 TUESDAY

22 WEDNESDAY

23 THURSDAY

FRIDAY 24

Christmas Day

SATURDAY 25

Boxing Day

SUNDAY 26

NOTES

BBC earth

W	T	F	S	S	M	T	W	T	F	S	S	M	T	W	T	F	S	S	**M**	**T**	**W**	**T**	**F**	**S**	**S**	M	T	W	T	F
1	2	3	4	5	6	7	8	9	10	11	12	13	14	15	16	17	18	19	**20**	**21**	**22**	**23**	**24**	**25**	**26**	27	28	29	30	31

27 MONDAY

Bank Holiday

28 TUESDAY

Bank Holiday

29 WEDNESDAY

30 THURSDAY

New Year's Eve

FRIDAY 31

New Year's Day

SATURDAY 1

SUNDAY 2

NOTES

BBC earth

T	F	S	S	M	T	W	T	F	S	S	**M**	**T**	**W**	**T**	**F**	**S**	**S**	M	T	W	T	F	S	S	M	T	W	T	F	S
16	17	18	19	20	21	22	23	24	25	26	**27**	**28**	**29**	**30**	**31**	**1**	**2**	3	4	5	6	7	8	9	10	11	12	13	14	15

PLANNER2022

JANUARY	FEBRUARY	MARCH
1 S	1 T	1 T
2 S	2 W	2 W
3 M	3 T	3 T
4 T	4 F	4 F
5 W	**5 S**	**5 S**
6 T	**6 S**	**6 S**
7 F	7 M	7 M
8 S	8 T	8 T
9 S	9 W	9 W
10 M	10 T	10 T
11 T	11 F	11 F
12 W	**12 S**	**12 S**
13 T	**13 S**	**13 S**
14 F	14 M	14 M
15 S	15 T	15 T
16 S	16 W	16 W
17 M	17 T	17 T
18 T	18 F	18 F
19 W	**19 S**	**19 S**
20 T	**20 S**	**20 S**
21 F	21 M	21 M
22 S	22 T	22 T
23 S	23 W	23 W
24 M	24 T	24 T
25 T	25 F	25 F
26 W	**26 S**	**26 S**
27 T	**27 S**	**27 S**
28 F	28 M	28 M
29 S		29 T
30 S		30 W
31 M		31 T

APRIL	MAY	JUNE
1 F	**1 S**	1 W
2 S	2 M	2 T
3 S	3 T	3 F
4 M	4 W	**4 S**
5 T	5 T	**5 S**
6 W	6 F	6 M
7 T	**7 S**	7 T
8 F	**8 S**	8 W
9 S	9 M	9 T
10 S	10 T	10 F
11 M	11 W	**11 S**
12 T	12 T	**12 S**
13 W	13 F	13 M
14 T	**14 S**	14 T
15 F	**15 S**	15 W
16 S	16 M	16 T
17 S	17 T	17 F
18 M	18 W	**18 S**
19 T	19 T	**19 S**
20 W	20 F	20 M
21 T	**21 S**	21 T
22 F	**22 S**	22 W
23 S	23 M	23 T
24 S	24 T	24 F
25 M	25 W	**25 S**
26 T	26 T	**26 S**
27 W	27 F	27 M
28 T	**28 S**	28 T
29 F	**29 S**	29 W
30 S	30 M	30 T
	31 T	

JULY	AUGUST	SEPTEMBER
1 F	1 M	1 T
2 S	2 T	2 F
3 S	3 W	**3 S**
4 M	4 T	**4 S**
5 T	5 F	5 M
6 W	**6 S**	6 T
7 T	**7 S**	7 W
8 F	8 M	8 T
9 S	9 T	9 F
10 S	10 W	**10 S**
11 M	11 T	**11 S**
12 T	12 F	12 M
13 W	**13 S**	13 T
14 T	**14 S**	14 W
15 F	15 M	15 T
16 S	16 T	16 F
17 S	17 W	**17 S**
18 M	18 T	**18 S**
19 T	19 F	19 M
20 W	**20 S**	20 T
21 T	**21 S**	21 W
22 F	22 M	22 T
23 S	23 T	23 F
24 S	24 W	**24 S**
25 M	25 T	**25 S**
26 T	26 F	26 M
27 W	**27 S**	27 T
28 T	**28 S**	28 W
29 F	29 M	29 T
30 S	30 T	30 F
31 S	31 W	

OCTOBER	NOVEMBER	DECEMBER
1 S	1 T	1 T
2 S	2 W	2 F
3 M	3 T	**3 S**
4 T	4 F	**4 S**
5 W	**5 S**	5 M
6 T	**6 S**	6 T
7 F	7 M	7 W
8 S	8 T	8 T
9 S	9 W	9 F
10 M	10 T	**10 S**
11 T	11 F	**11 S**
12 W	**12 S**	12 M
13 T	**13 S**	13 T
14 F	14 M	14 W
15 S	15 T	15 T
16 S	16 W	16 F
17 M	17 T	**17 S**
18 T	18 F	**18 S**
19 W	**19 S**	19 M
20 T	**20 S**	20 T
21 F	21 M	21 W
22 S	22 T	22 T
23 S	23 W	23 F
24 M	24 T	**24 S**
25 T	25 F	**25 S**
26 W	**26 S**	26 M
27 T	**27 S**	27 T
28 F	28 M	28 W
29 S	29 T	29 T
30 S	30 W	30 F
31 M		**31 S**

ADDRESS/PHONE NUMBERS

Name

Address

Telephone Mobile

Email

Name

Address

Telephone Mobile

Email

Name

Address

Telephone Mobile

Email

Name

Address

Telephone Mobile

Email

Name

Address

Telephone Mobile

Email

Name

Address

Telephone Mobile

Email

Name

Address

Telephone Mobile

Email

Name

Address

Telephone Mobile

Email

Name

Address

Telephone Mobile

Email

Name

Address

Telephone Mobile

Email

Name

Address

Telephone Mobile

Email

Name

Address

Telephone Mobile

Email

NOTES

NOTES

NOTES

NOTES